STUDY GUIDE

FORGIVEN™

THE TRANSFORMING POWER OF CONFESSION

AUGUSTINE INSTITUTE

FORGIVEN

THE TRANSFORMING POWER OF CONFESSION

Nihil Obstat: Fr. Gary B. Selin, S.T.D, *Censor Deputatus*
October 5, 2017
Imprimatur: Most Reverend Samuel J. Aquila, S.T.L., Archbishop of Denver

Writers: Ashley Crane, Lucas Pollice
Print Production/Graphic Design: Jeff Cole, Brenda Kraft, Christina Gray, Jane Myers, Devin Schadt, Kathleen McCarty, Ann Diaz
Media: Aurora Cerulla, Steve Flanigan, Jon Ervin, Matthew Krekeler, Justin Leddick, Kevin Mallory, Ted Mast, Edward Sri, Molly Sweeney

6160 South Syracuse Way, Suite 310
Greenwood Village, CO 80111
Information: 303-937-4420
formed.org

Printed in the United States of America
ISBN 978-0-9972037-8-3

TABLE OF CONTENTS

FORGIVEN: AN INTRODUCTION

Welcome to the FORGIVEN™ program. These sessions have been carefully designed to help you more richly encounter God's mercy in Confession and, if you are a parent, to also help you prepare for your child's First Confession. They will explore the profound effects and healing grace of the Sacrament of Reconciliation.

In this program you will discover the merciful way that God seeks us out when we have sinned and calls us back to himself. You will examine the sacrament from the perspective of both the priest and the penitent, and you will explore the scriptural foundation of the sacrament. This study will help you recognize the beauty of the Rite of Penance and the transformative power of the grace God offers us in this sacrament.

What You'll Find in Each FORGIVEN Session

OPENING PRAYER: The prayer is included in both the Leader Guide and the Study Guide. You can read along silently or aloud.

INTRODUCTION: Follow along with the Introduction for an overview of what you'll experience in the session.

CONNECT: Each session begins with questions that help you get to know one another on a deeper level.

VIDEO: Together you'll watch an engaging video segment that teaches the subject using Sacred Scripture and Sacred Tradition of the Catholic Church along with compelling stories and testimonials. This Study Guide includes a brief outline that follows the key points in the teaching and has room for note-taking.

DISCUSS: Talk in small groups about the video teaching; questions for reflection on the topic are in this guide.

COMMIT—ENCOUNTERING GOD'S MERCY: This will help you to more fully understand the Sacrament of Reconciliation and helps you to more deeply relate to Christ and the Church. You'll preview this with your group.

WRAP-UP AND CLOSING PRAYER: After reviewing the main points of the session together, you will close in prayer. You'll find the words to prayer in this guide, so feel free to read along silently or aloud.

DIGGING DEEPER: In this Study Guide we've also included quotations by the saints and excerpts from the *Catechism of the Catholic Church* and other Catholic works as they relate to each session topic.

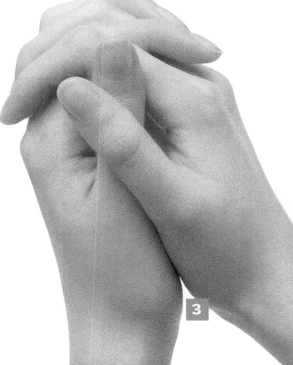

FOR FURTHER STUDY: Each session concludes with suggested resources for continued study and reflection, which may be of interest to participants, parents, and leaders.

NOTES

FORGIVEN™

THE TRANSFORMING POWER OF CONFESSION

SESSION 1
Where Are You?

OPENING PRAYER

Out of the depths I cry to you, O LORD!
Lord, hear my voice!
Let your ears be attentive to the voice
of my supplications!
If you, O LORD, should mark iniquities,
Lord, who could stand?
But there is forgiveness with you,
that you may be feared.
I wait for the LORD, my soul waits,
and in his word I hope;
my soul waits for the LORD
more than watchmen for the morning,
more than watchmen for the morning.

O Israel, hope in the LORD!
For with the LORD there is mercy,
and with him is plenteous redemption.
And he will redeem Israel from all his iniquities.

Amen.

—Psalm 130

INTRODUCTION

Have you ever received a "wake-up call" that inspired you to make a change in your life? Maybe it was something significant like a health issue that forced you to make better choices. Or perhaps a comment from a friend convinced you to take a different course of action on something. When we go off course in life, God often sends us a wake-up call to draw us back. But sometimes it's difficult—even painful—to stop, listen, and turn around. Thankfully, God doesn't ask us to do it on our own. He not only calls us home, but he also walks with us every step of the way.

Can you share an experience that was a "wake-up" call in your life?

What do you think is the most important thing about being a Christian?

> "In the life of the body a man is sometimes sick, and unless he takes medicine, he will die. Even so in the spiritual life a man is sick on account of sin. For that reason he needs medicine so that he may be restored to health; and this grace is bestowed in the Sacrament of Penance."
>
> —St. Thomas Aquinas

VIDEO

Watch the video. The following is a brief outline of the topics covered.

I. Wake-up Call

A. Guilt can be God's way of getting our attention

B. Signals that something needs to change

C. How do we handle guilt?

    1. Find distractions

    2. Rationalize our behavior

    3. Blame others

    4. Admit we're wrong

VIDEO CONTINUED

II. Sin

    A. About breaking a relationship, not just breaking a rule

    B. Leads us to hide from God, like Adam and Eve

III. God's Perspective

    A. Above all else, God is love

    B. "Father" is who God *is;* "Lawmaker," "Judge," etc., is what he *does*

    C. "Where are you?"

        1. When we sin, God seeks us out

        2. The only sin God can't forgive is the one for which we won't ask forgiveness

"Confession is an act of honesty and courage—an act of entrusting ourselves, beyond sin, to the mercy of a loving and forgiving God. It is an act of the prodigal son, who returns to his Father and is welcomed by Him with the kiss of peace."
—Pope St. John Paul II (from a homily in San Antonio on September 13, 1987)

DISCUSS

1. What is your interpretation of this statement? "When we sin, God does not love us less, but we love ourselves less."

_____

_____

_____

2. "There comes a time when one must take a position that is neither safe, nor politic, nor popular, but he must take it because conscience tells him it is right." – Martin Luther King Jr., *A Testament of Hope: The Essential Writings and Speeches* In light of this quote, why is a well-formed conscience essential for our happiness?

_____

_____

_____

3. "God doesn't just want more *from us,* he wants more *for* us!" What do you think this quote means?

_____

_____

_____

"Conscience is a judgment of reason whereby the human person recognizes the moral quality of a concrete act that he is going to perform, is in the process of performing, or has already completed."

—CCC 1778

COMMIT—*ENCOUNTERING GOD'S MERCY*

Consider God's call to Adam and Eve after they had sinned: *"And they heard the sound of the LORD God walking in the garden in the cool of the day, and the man and his wife hid themselves from the presence of the LORD God among the trees of the garden. But the LORD God called to the man, and said to him, 'Where are you?'"* (Genesis 3:8–9).

Adam and Eve's first impulse after their sin is to hide themselves from God. They feel that same guilt we experience when we know we've done something wrong, and it causes us to be separated from him. **Do you ever feel a desire to hide yourself from God? Why or why not?** Write your reflections in the space below.

_____

_____

_____

When God comes to the Garden, he already knows Adam and Eve's sin. He seeks them out not to call them to account for their actions and pay the price for their mistake; he isn't looking to scold them or punish them. God is calling them back—out of shame and hiding, back to himself. He wants to repair the damage that sin has done.

God loves us so much that he won't let anything at all stand between us and his love. Before Adam and Eve have even expressed sorrow for their sin, God seeks them out. This is the incredible beauty of God's mercy! As St. Paul says in his letter to the Romans: *"But God shows his love for us in that while we were yet sinners Christ died for us"* (Romans 5:8).

God doesn't wait for us to come back to him after we have sinned—he comes looking for us, just as he looked for Adam and Eve. In his merciful love he searches for us to bring us home. He is calling to each one of us: "Where are you?" **What is your answer? What are some areas of your life that you need to surrender to God's merciful love?**

_____

_____

_____

_____

CLOSING PRAYER

Have mercy on me, O God, according to your merciful love;
according to your abundant mercy blot out my transgressions.
Wash me thoroughly from my iniquity, and cleanse me from my sin!

For I know my transgressions, and my sin is ever before me.
Against you, you only, have I sinned, and done that which is evil in your sight,
so that you are justified in your sentence and blameless in your judgment . . .

Purge me with hyssop, and I shall be clean; wash me, and I shall be whiter than snow.
Make me hear joy and gladness; let the bones which you have broken rejoice.
Hide your face from my sins, and blot out all my iniquities.

Create in me a clean heart, O God, and put a new and right spirit within me.
Cast me not away from your presence, and take not your holy Spirit from me.
Restore to me the joy of your salvation, and uphold me with a willing spirit . . .

O Lord, open my lips, and my mouth shall show forth your praise.

Amen.

—Psalm 51:1–4, 7–12, 15

FOR FURTHER STUDY

Catechism of the Catholic Church, 1422–1429

Pope St. John Paul II, *Reconciliatio et Paenitentia (Reconciliation and Penance)*,
Post-Synodal Apostolic Exhortation (1984)

Parable of the Prodigal Son, Luke 15:11–32

NOTES

FORGIVEN™
THE TRANSFORMING POWER OF CONFESSION

SESSION 2
An Encounter with Mercy

SESSION 2 | AN ENCOUNTER WITH MERCY

OPENING PRAYER

Lord Jesus Christ,
You show us the glory of the Father,
the God of mercy and forgiveness,
the God who is love.
Help us to trust fully in your divine mercy
and rely completely on your unending love.
Teach us to be merciful,
as the Father is merciful,
that the whole world may know
and trust in your merciful love.
We ask this through the intercession of
Mary, Mother of Mercy.

Amen.

INTRODUCTION

God loves us right where we are, but he loves us too much to leave us there. In the last session we looked at guilt as a wakeup call—a way to turn our attention back to God when we have sinned. In this session we will look more closely at God's invitation to encounter his mercy and healing in a very real and tangible way in the Sacrament of Reconciliation.

14

"Therefore, if any one is in Christ, he is a new creation; the old has passed away, behold, the new has come. All this is from God, who through Christ reconciled us to himself and gave us the ministry of reconciliation; that is, in Christ God was reconciling the world to himself, not counting their trespasses against them, and entrusting to us the message of reconciliation. So we are ambassadors for Christ, God making his appeal through us. We beg you on behalf of Christ, be reconciled to God. For our sake he made him to be sin who knew no sin, so that in him we might become the righteousness of God."

—2 Corinthians 5:17–21

CONNECT

Can you describe a time when you were very aware of the presence of God with you?

Who is someone that has helped you most in life?

"In her motherly care, the Church grants us the mercy of God which prevails over all our sins and is especially at work in the sacrament of reconciliation."
—CCC 2040

SESSION 2 | AN ENCOUNTER WITH MERCY

Watch the teaching on video.
The following is a brief outline of topics covered.

I. Woman Caught in Adultery (John 8)

    A. What was she feeling?

    B. Unexpected encounter with God's love and mercy

        1. Jesus did not condemn her

        2. He also did not condone her sins

    C. God sees us as we are and loves us

    D. Confession offers a new beginning

        1. We are not our sins

        2. Mercy invites us to a much greater life

II. God's Mercy

    A. God is merciful

    B. God is constantly seeking us out

    C. We encounter Jesus himself in the Sacrament of Reconciliation

    D. Jesus gave the Apostles his own authority and power to forgive sins

        1. God has always used mediators

        2. The priest acts in the Person of Christ the Head

III. Human Aspect of the Sacrament

A. God knows we need a tangible experience of mercy and forgiveness

B. Confession gives us a physical encounter along with the supernatural reality of grace

C. We have a human need to say that we're sorry

D. We have a human need to actually hear someone say that we are forgiven

IV. Healing

A. In Confession Jesus forgives our sins

B. He also wants to address the root causes of our sin and heal the wounds of sin in our soul

C. The Sacrament gives us the grace to "go and sin no more"

D. God offers us his mercy so that we can extend his mercy to the world

SESSION 2 | AN ENCOUNTER WITH MERCY

DISCUSS

1. According to psychologists, an identity crisis occurs when someone is unsure of their role in life and feel as if they don't really know themselves. In other words, someone experiencing an "identity crisis" is unable to provide an answer to the question "Who are you?" What difference do you think Jesus makes to the formation of a strong identity?

_____

_____

_____

2. Holiness and sin have an inverse relationship. As one increases, the other decreases. That being said, it was common for many of the saints to go to Confession frequently. For example, Pope St. John Paul II and St. Teresa of Calcutta are known to have gone to Confession once a week. How do we explain this apparent contradiction?

_____

_____

_____

3. In Confession, why does the priest say "I absolve you of your sin" and not "God absolves you of your sin"?

_____

_____

_____

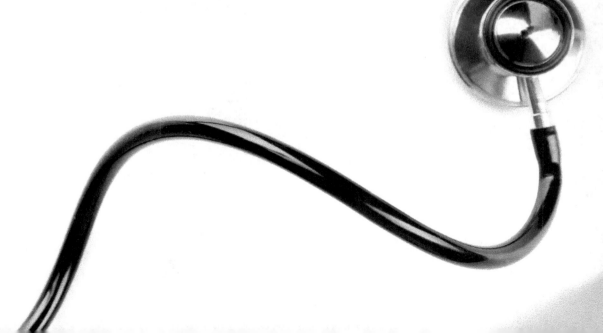

COMMIT—*ENCOUNTERING GOD'S MERCY*

The story of the woman caught in adultery in John 8:2–11 presents us with a beautiful image of the mercy and grace offered to us in the Sacrament of Reconciliation. Read through this passage slowly and prayerfully:

"Early in the morning [Jesus] came again to the temple; all the people came to him, and he sat down and taught them. The scribes and the Pharisees brought a woman who had been caught in adultery, and placing her in the midst they said to him, 'Teacher, this woman has been caught in the act of adultery. Now in the law Moses commanded us to stone such. What do you say about her?' This they said to test him, that they might have some charge to bring against him. Jesus bent down and wrote with his finger on the ground. And as they continued to ask him, he stood up and said to them, 'Let him who is without sin among you be the first to throw a stone at her.' And once more he bent down and wrote with his finger on the ground. But when they heard it, they went away, one by one, beginning with the eldest, and Jesus was left alone with the woman standing before him. Jesus looked up and said to her, 'Woman, where are they? Has no one condemned you?' She said, 'No one, Lord.' And Jesus said, 'Neither do I condemn you; go, and do not sin again.'"

—John 8:2–11

Imagine yourself in this passage. **Have you ever felt like this woman: caught in your sins, accused by others, condemning yourself for mistakes you've made? What might she have been thinking and feeling when the scribes and Pharisees brought her before Jesus to make their point? How do you think she felt when everyone else left and she was left alone with Jesus? What may have gone through her mind when she heard his words, "Neither do I condemn you; go, and do not sin again"?** Write your reflections in the space below.

_____

_____

_____

COMMIT - CONTINUED

Jesus rescues this woman in two ways. He forgives rather than condemns her, but he also silences her accusers. The forgiveness we receive in Confession reconciles us with God, but it also means there is no longer anything for the accuser, Satan, to hold over us. And it also means that we no longer need to accuse ourselves for our sins. They are washed away, and we are free. In place of our guilt God gives us his healing grace. Mercy makes us free to love.

God offers us his mercy so that we, in turn, can offer his mercy to a world desperately in need. **Take a few moments to prayerfully reflect on the ways God has shown you his mercy. Ask the Holy Spirit to show you one person to whom you can extend God's mercy.** This may be someone who has wronged you, someone who needs to hear the message of God's mercy, someone in need of a kind, encouraging word, etc. **What concrete thing can you do to share God's mercy with this person?**

_____

_____

_____

_____

_____

> ""My Heart overflows with great mercy for souls, and especially for poor sinners. If only they could understand that I am the best of Fathers to them and that it is for them that the Blood and Water flowed from My Heart as from a fount overflowing with mercy. For them I dwell in the tabernacle as King of Mercy."
> —*Diary of St. Faustina, 367*

CLOSING PRAYER

Bless the LORD, O my soul;
and all that is within me, bless his holy name!
Bless the LORD, O my soul, and forget not all his benefits,
who forgives all your iniquity, who heals all your diseases,
who redeems your life from the Pit,
who crowns you with mercy and compassion,
who satisfies you with good as long as you live
so that your youth is renewed like the eagle's.

The LORD is merciful and gracious,
slow to anger and abounding in mercy.

For as high as the heavens are high above the earth,
so great is his mercy toward those who fear him;
as far as the east is from the west,
so far does he remove our transgressions from us.

Bless the LORD, O my soul!

Amen.

—Psalm 103:1–5, 8, 11–12, 22

FOR FURTHER STUDY

Catechism of the Catholic Church, 1440–1445

John 8:1–11

Michael E. Gaitley MIC, *The Second Greatest Story Ever Told: Now Is the Time of Mercy* (Stockbridge, MA: Marian Press, 2015)

Pope Francis, *The Name of God Is Mercy* (New York: Random House, 2016)

Pope St. John Paul II, *Dives in Misericordia* (1980)

St. Maria Faustina Kowalska, *Diary: Divine Mercy in My Soul* (Stockbridge, MA: Marian Press: 2005)

Lighthouse Talks:
    Scott Hahn, *The Healing Power of Confession*
    Father Larry Richards, *Confession*

NOTES

FORGIVEN™

THE TRANSFORMING POWER OF CONFESSION

SESSION 3
The Rite Explained

OPENING PRAYER

Blessed is he whose transgression
is forgiven, whose sin is covered.
Blessed is the man to whom the LORD
imputes no iniquity,
and in whose spirit there is no deceit.
When I declared not my sin,
my body wasted away through my groaning all day long.
For day and night your hand was heavy upon me;
my strength was dried up as by the heat of summer.
I acknowledged my sin to you, and I did not hide my iniquity;
I said, "I will confess my transgressions to the LORD";
then you forgave the guilt of my sin.
Therefore let every one who is godly offer prayer to you;
at a time of distress, in the rush of great waters,
they shall not reach him.
You are a hiding place for me,
you preserve me from trouble;
you surround me with deliverance.

—Psalm 32:1–7

INTRODUCTION

It's not easy to admit when we've done something wrong—
or failed to do something right. But when we learn to trust in
God's mercy, we don't have to be afraid to face our sins. That
mercy is present to us in a very real way in the confessional
through the ministry of the priest. God's merciful love shapes
every word and action of the sacrament, and when we
prepare for it honestly and prayerfully, we will be open to
receiving the fullness of his grace.

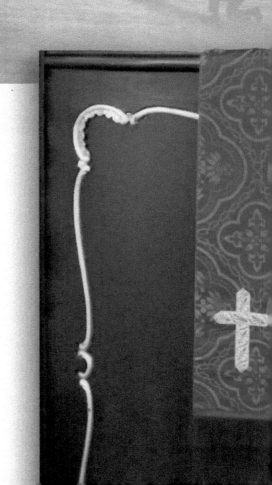

Some wounds are deeper than others. Because mortal sin destroys the life of grace in the soul and ruptures our relationship to God and his Church, we need God's minister (the priest) to absolve us formally when we've committed mortal sin. Confession is the ordinary means of forgiveness in the Church, and one of the precepts of the Church requires us to confess mortal sins at least once a year.

Anyone who is aware of having committed a mortal sin should not receive the Eucharist, even if he thinks he has perfect contrition, without first receiving absolution in the Sacrament of Reconciliation. **(see CCC 1856–1859, 1452–1453, 1457)**

CONNECT

Can you describe a time when you had to take a risk and trust?

What would you like the courage to do?

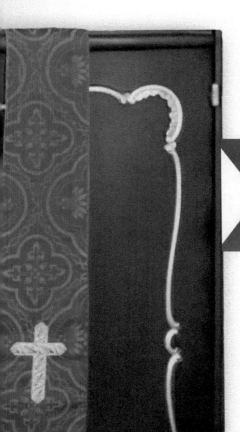

"He who conceals his transgressions will not prosper, but he who confesses and forsakes them will obtain mercy."
—Proverbs 28:13

Watch the teaching on video.
The following is a brief outline of topics covered.

I. Priests' Perspective on Confession

A. It's a joy and privilege to welcome people back to God in the sacrament

B. Nothing new under the sun—you aren't going to shock the priest with your sin

C. Absolutely confidential (Seal of Confession)

D. Admiration for the courage of the penitent

E. Many priests forget everything they hear in the confessional

F. Sin is forgiven to make us free to love

II. The Sacrament

A. Examination of Conscience

    1. We prepare for the Sacrament because we take the encounter with Christ seriously

    2. Consider what sins we have committed

    3. Keep in mind that we are approaching our loving Father

    4. "In my thoughts"—our words and actions have their root in our thoughts

    5. "In my words"—we can sin through our speech

    6. "In what I have done"—sins of commission; what we most commonly consider as sin

    7. "In what I have failed to do"—sins of omission

B. Sign of the Cross

C. "Bless me Father, for I have sinned. It has been . . . since my last confession"—gives the priest context

D. State our sins

    1. Simple, straightforward, honest

    2. Humbling but not humiliating

    3. List the most serious first, and if you forget a small sin don't worry about it

E. Penance

    1. Act of love and thanksgiving in response to God's forgiveness

    2. Addresses some of the practical consequences of sin

F. Act of Contrition

    1. Like a formal apology

    2. Can use a memorized prayer or make up your own

G. Absolution

    1. Priest raises his hand over penitent—invokes God's presence

    2. Recites the prayer of Absolution—this is the moment of forgiveness

        a. Father of mercies

        b. Pardon and peace

        c. Ministry of the Church

Whenever we make an examination of conscience, we can also look at other aspects of sin to see what we should bring to Confession. The *Catechism* tells us that we can distinguish between sins: (1) according to their object, the virtues they oppose, or the commandments they violate; (2) whether they concern God, neighbor, or self; (3) whether they are spiritual or carnal sins; and (4) whether they relate to thought, word, deed, or omission **(see CCC 1853).**

DISCUSS

1. In the video we heard that God forgives our sin in order to clear the way for love. Grace increases in our souls similar to the way a fire increases in brightness and heat with the addition of more fuel. Since sanctifying grace is God's very life, how are we to understand an increase of God's life within us when he is already omnipresent and infinite?

_____

_____

_____

2. God's will for our lives is to grow in self-awareness, self-possession, and self-donation. In other words, it is difficult to give ourselves away in love if we are not free to love. And, it is difficult to grow in the freedom necessary to love if we are not aware of what restrains us. How does understanding the purpose of our lives emphasize the importance of a good examination of conscience?

_____

_____

_____

3. A presidential candidate was asked the question: "How do you define sin?" His answer was: "Being out of alignment with my values." What is problematic with this answer?

_____

_____

_____

"Confession heals, confession justifies, confession grants pardon of sin, all hope consists in confession; in confession there is a chance for mercy."
—St. Isidore of Seville

COMMIT—ENCOUNTERING GOD'S MERCY

An examination of conscience is a prayerful reflection on our life, looking for sins that we might have committed in our thoughts, words, actions, or inaction. There are many different kinds of examinations of conscience—some are structured around the Ten Commandments; some are based on the seven capital (or deadly) sins. A simple way to begin looking for sin is to look at our thoughts, words, actions, and inaction through the lens of the two greatest commandments: **"The first is, 'Hear, O Israel: The Lord our God, the Lord is one; and you shall love the Lord your God with all your heart, and with all your soul, and with all your mind, and with all your strength.' The second is this, 'You shall love your neighbor as yourself'"** (Mark 12:29–31). Take some time in quiet prayer to reflect on these verses. Begin by asking the Holy Spirit to help you make this examination of conscience:

Spirit of truth, guide me as I examine my life. Give me the wisdom to see all my thoughts, words, actions, and inaction as you do. Give me the courage to acknowledge my sins. Give me the humility and strength to confess my sins. And give me the grace to trust wholeheartedly in your mercy and forgiveness. Amen.

Prayerfully consider, **"In what ways have I not loved God with my whole heart, soul, mind, and strength? In what ways have I failed to love my neighbor as myself?"** Write your reflections in the space below. You can use these private reflections to help you make your next confession.

_____

_____

_____

How did you feel before starting the examination of conscience? How did you feel after you finished it? What do you think it means to see our sins the way God sees them?

_____

"Go to your confessor; open your heart to him; display to him all the recesses of your soul; take the advice that he will give you with the utmost humility and simplicity. For God, who has an infinite love for obedience, frequently renders profitable the counsels we take from others, but especially from those who are the guides of our souls."

—St. Francis de Sales

CLOSING PRAYER

The Confiteor

I confess to almighty God,
and to you, my brothers and sisters,
that I have greatly sinned,
in my thoughts and in my words,
in what I have done and in what I have failed to do,
through my fault, through my fault,
through my most grievous fault;
therefore I ask blessed Mary ever-Virgin,
all the Angels and Saints,
and you, my brothers and sisters,
to pray for me to the Lord our God.

Amen.

—*Roman Missal, 4*

FOR FURTHER STUDY

Catechism of the Catholic Church, 1480–1484, 1846–1869

Christopher Walsh, *The Untapped Power of the Sacrament of Penance: A Priest's View* (Cincinnati, OH: Servant Books, 2005)

Go to USCCB.org to find several examinations of conscience in the Prayer and Worship/Sacraments section

John A. Kane, *How to Make a Good Confession: A Pocket Guide to Reconciliation with God* (Manchester, NH: Sophia Institute Press, 2001)

Augustine Institute: *How to Make a Good Confession* Booklet

Lighthouse Talks: *7 Secrets of Confession* by Vinny Flynn

Examination of Conscience Based on the Ten Commandments

1. I am the LORD your God. You shall have no false gods before me. Do I put God before my spouse? My children? My work? Do I believe that God loves me? Do I have any "false gods" in my life like money, fame, power, possessions? Have I been involved in fortune-telling, astrology, palm-reading, or witchcraft? Do I pray daily?

2. You shall not take the name of the LORD your God in vain. Do I use curse words? Have I made oaths or sworn promises to God that I haven't kept? Have I allowed others to swear in my presence?

3. Remember to keep holy the LORD's Day. Do I attend Mass on Sundays and Holy Days of Obligation? Do I avoid unnecessary work on Sundays? Do I avoid unnecessary shopping on Sundays?

4. Honor your father and mother. Do I show love to my parents, regardless of their age? Do I help them when I can? Do I respect my employer and others in authority? If I am a parent, have I given a bad example in word or deed to my children? Am I raising my children in the Catholic Faith?

5. You shall not kill. Have I killed or seriously injured anyone? Do I gossip? Have I had an abortion or helped someone get an abortion? Have I lost my temper, given in to anger, or harbored resentment against my neighbor? Do I bear grudges? Have I ever harmed anyone physically, mentally, or emotionally? Do I take care of the environment?

6. You shall not commit adultery. Have I used pornography? Have I watched movies that are overly violent or sexual? Have I consented to lustful thoughts? Have I masturbated? Have I had premarital sex? Have I treated anyone as an object, rather than a person? Do I eat or drink in excess? Have I lost sobriety through drunkenness or drug use?

7. You shall not steal. Have I stolen anything? Do I always give a full day's work for a full day's pay? Do I cheat in school or business? Am I fair in paying my employees? Am I honest in paying my taxes? Have I wasted time? Have I been generous in serving the poor?

8. You shall not bear false witness against your neighbor. Have I told a lie, even a white lie? Have I told lies to avoid getting in trouble? Have I revealed other people's secrets? Have I failed to mind my own business? Have I accused someone falsely? Have I judged others harshly? Have I been prejudiced or discriminated against anyone?

9. You shall not covet your neighbor's wife. Have I been unfaithful to my spouse in either my actions or my thoughts? Have I used my wife or husband merely to satisfy my sexual urges? Have I acted inappropriately with those of the opposite sex?

10. You shall not covet your neighbor's property. Have I envied anyone else's possessions, money, fame, or success? Have I used more than my fair share of resources?

NOTES

FORGIVEN™

THE TRANSFORMING POWER OF CONFESSION

SESSION 4
Biblical Foundations:
Sin, Mercy, and the
Sacrament of Confession

OPENING PRAYER

Hear my prayer, O LORD; give ear to my supplications!
In thy faithfulness answer me, in your righteousness!
Enter not into judgment with your servant;
for no man living is righteous before you.

For the enemy has pursued me; he has crushed my life to the
ground; he has made me sit in darkness like those long dead.
Therefore my spirit faints within me; my heart within me
is appalled.

I remember the days of old, I meditate on all that you
have done;
I muse on what your hands have wrought.
I stretch out my hands to you; my soul thirsts for you like a
parched land.

Make haste to answer me, O LORD! My spirit fails!
Hide not your face from me, lest I be like those who go down
to the Pit. Let me hear in the morning of your merciful love,
for in you I put my trust. Teach me the way I should go,
for to you I lift up my soul.

Amen.

INTRODUCTION

Have you ever wondered, "Where is *that* in the Bible?!"
When it comes to the Sacrament of Reconciliation, Catholics
and non-Catholics alike often want to know how confessing
our sins to a priest lines up with Scripture passages such as
"Who can forgive sins but God alone?" (Mark 2:7).
Confession has its roots in God's revelation of his mercy as
well as his authority in Scripture—and a closer look quickly
shows just how biblical this sacrament really is.

How has your perception of God changed from your childhood to the present?

How has your perception of yourself changed from your childhood to the present?

"Pray with great confidence, with confidence based upon the goodness and infinite generosity of God and upon the promises of Jesus Christ. God is a spring of living water which flows unceasingly into the hearts of those who pray."

—St. Louis de Montfort

VIDEO

Watch the video. The following is a brief outline of the topics covered.

I. Sin and Mercy in Scripture

A. Adam and Eve sinned, and God showed them mercy

B. This pattern is repeated throughout Scripture: Israel sins, and God responds with mercy

C. Greatest example is at Mount Sinai

DELEGATE

VIDEO CONTINUED

II. Exodus 34:6–7

    A. Becomes one of the most important passages in the Old Testament

    B. Eight key attributes of God

        1. Merciful

        2. Gracious

        3. Slow to Anger

        4. Abounding in steadfast love

        5. Faithfulness

        6. Storing up steadfast love for 1,000 generations

        7. Forgiving iniquity and transgression and sin

        8. Does not clear the guilty (those who don't ask for forgiveness)

    C. All the prophetic books quote this passage to remind Israel of God's mercy

III. *Shuv*

    A. "Repentance" in Hebrew

    B. Literally "to turn about"

    C. Repentance is about changing from our way to God's way

IV. David

A. Greatly blessed and favored by God

B. But then he commits adultery and murders to cover it up

C. David admits his sin and repents (2 Samuel 12)—in contrast to Saul who denies his sin

D. David has courage to confess because he has hope in God's mercy

   1. Psalm 51:1—**"Have mercy on me, O God"**

   2. Themes of mercy and forgiveness in Psalm 51 echo attributes of God revealed in Exodus 34:6–7

E. David shows us what it means to trust in God's forgiveness

   1. David's last words, 2 Samuel 22 (also Psalm 18)

   2. 2 Samuel 22:21–27—David says he is blameless and pure

   3. He can say this because he trusts that God's forgiveness truly cleanses him from his sin

   4. Psalm 103:12—**"As far as the east is from the west, so far does he remove our transgressions from us"**

V. Exile

A. Nehemiah 9—Ezra reminds the people of Exodus 34:6–7 and the pattern of Israel's sin and God's forgiveness

B. Exile is the physical manifestation of the reality of sin—being far from God

C. The return from exile is the *shuv*—the people are brought back to Jerusalem as a sign of repentance and returning to God

D. The real scandal of Scripture is God's mercy

VIDEO CONTINUED

PART II

I. Why do we confess our sins to a priest?

A. Matthew 9:1–8—the paralytic lowered through the roof of Peter's house

    1. Physical healing is a sign that Jesus also has the power and authority to forgive sins

    2. Son of man—reference to Daniel 7:13–14

    3. "They glorified God, who had given such authority to men" (Matthew 9:8)

B. Authority in Matthew's Gospel

    1. Matthew 8–9 shows Jesus's authority through ten miracles

    2. Number ten signifies authority

    3. Jesus has authority from the Father, and he has the authority to delegate that authority

    4. Matthew 10—Jesus gives his authority to the twelve Apostles and sends them out

C. Authority in Luke's Gospel

    1. Luke 10—Jesus sends out seventy disciples with his authority

    2. Jesus sends his disciples as his ambassadors—they speak his words

    3. 2 Corinthians 5:18–20—Paul talks about his ministry as an ambassador of Christ's reconciliation

D. Authority in John's Gospel

    1. John 17:18—Jesus sends the Apostles as the Father sent him *(apostello,* Greek meaning "to send")

    2. In the Old Testament, the angels bear the presence and word of God, speaking and acting on his behalf

    3. In the New Testament, the Apostles now bear the presence and word of God, speaking and acting on his behalf

    4. Jesus shares his divine authority with men

    5. John 20:22–23—Jesus gives his Apostles authority to forgive sins

DISCUSS

1. Author Richard Dawkins writes in *The God Delusion:* "The God of the Old Testament is arguably the most unpleasant character in all fiction." As an atheist, Dawkins writes this to undermine Christianity and the Bible. How can we reconcile the God of the Old Testament and the merciful love of our heavenly Father revealed to us through Jesus Christ?

_____

_____

_____

2. God says this of David, the great king of Israel: "I have found in David the son of Jesse a man after my heart, who will do all my will" (Acts 13:22). And yet, David failed miserably in doing God's will when he committed adultery with Bathsheba and had her husband killed so that he could take her to be his wife. Given these circumstances, how is David a role model for us?

_____

_____

_____

3. The great rabbi Maimonides is credited with this profound statement: "Give a man a fish and you feed him for a day; teach a man to fish and you feed him for a lifetime." How does this statement give insight into the reasons Jesus delegated his priesthood?

_____

_____

_____

"God's patience has to call forth in us the courage to return to him, however many mistakes and sins there may be in our life. . . . It is there, in the wounds of Jesus, that we are truly secure; there we encounter the boundless love of his heart. Thomas understood this. Saint Bernard goes on to ask: But what can I count on? My own merits? No, 'My merit is God's mercy. I am by no means lacking merits as long as he is rich in mercy. If the mercies of the Lord are manifold, I too will abound in merits.' This is important: the courage to trust in Jesus' mercy, to trust in his patience, to seek refuge always in the wounds of his love."

—Pope Francis, *Homily on Divine Mercy Sunday*, April 7, 2013

COMMIT—*ENCOUNTERING GOD'S MERCY*

In the video Tim Gray said that Exodus 34:6–7 becomes the most important passage in the Old Testament for understanding who God is. Read through this passage two or three times slowly and prayerfully.

"The LORD passed before him, and proclaimed, 'The LORD, the LORD, a God merciful and gracious, slow to anger, and abounding in mercy and faithfulness, keeping merciful love for thousands, forgiving iniquity and transgression and sin, but who will by no means clear the guilty." (Exodus 34:6–7)

Which of the eight key characteristics of God revealed in this passage stands out the most to you? Why?

_____

_____

Psalm 18 is a prayer of David thanking God for delivering him from his physical enemy, Saul. When he prayed it again at the end of his life, David surely understood the necessity of thanking God not only for rescuing him physically throughout his life but, even more importantly, delivering him from his sins. Read through Psalm 18, and then compose your own short psalm of thanksgiving to God for his saving mercy toward you.

_____

CLOSING PRAYER

I love you, O LORD, my strength.
The LORD is my rock, and my fortress, and my deliverer,
my God, my rock, in whom I take refuge,
my shield, and the horn of my salvation, my stronghold.
I call upon the LORD, who is worthy to be praised,
and I am saved from my enemies.

The LORD rewarded me according to my righteousness;
according to the cleanness of my hands he recompensed me.
For I have kept the ways of the LORD, and have not wickedly departed from my God.
For all his ordinances were before me, and his statues I did not put away from me.
I was blameless before him, and I kept myself from guilt.
Therefore the LORD has recompensed me according to my righteousness,
according to the cleanness of my hands in his sight.

With the loyal you show yourself loyal;
with the blameless man you show yourself blameless;
with the pure you show yourself pure;
and with the crooked you show yourself perverse.
For you deliver a humble people; but the haughty eyes you bring down.
Yes, you light my lamp; the LORD my God lightens my darkness.
Yes, by you I can crush a troop; and by my God I can leap over a wall.
This God—his way is perfect; the promise of the LORD proves true;
he is a shield for all those who take refuge in him.

Amen.

—Psalm 18:1–3, 20–30

FOR FURTHER STUDY

Tim Gray, "Sacrament of Penance and Reconciliation" in *Sacraments in Scripture: Salvation History Made Present* (Steubenville, OH: Emmaus Road Publishing, 2001)

Scott Hahn, *Lord Have Mercy: The Healing Power of Confession* (New York: Doubleday, 2003)

Catechism of the Catholic Church on the Sacrament of Penance and Reconciliation, 1440–1445

NOTES

FORGIVEN™
THE TRANSFORMING POWER OF CONFESSION

SESSION 5
Answering Common Questions about Confession

OPENING PRAYER

Lord God,
I hope by your grace for the pardon of all my sins
And after life here to gain eternal happiness
Because you have promised it
Who are infinitely powerful, faithful, kind, and merciful.
In this hope I intend to live and die.

Amen.

—Act of Hope

INTRODUCTION

In 1 John 4:8 we read that **"God is love."** This is the beginning
of the answer to every possible question about the Sacrament
of Reconciliation. Over the course of this study we have looked
at God's love and mercy, how he seeks us out and calls us back
to himself when we sin, how to prepare for and participate in
the Sacrament of Reconciliation, and where we find its basis in
Scripture. It all begins in God's love for us and his desire to forgive
and heal us in this sacrament. Why do we need to go to a priest?
Why is the sacrament designed the way that it is? The first part of
the answer is: because God is love.

CONNECT

Have you identified a particular calling or purpose for your life?

What appeals to you most about spending eternity in Heaven?

"Our Lord Himself I saw in . . . this venerable Sacrament . . . I felt as if my chains fell, as those of St. Peter at the touch of the Divine messenger. My God, what new scenes for my soul!"
—St. Louis de Montfort

VIDEO

Watch the video. The following is a brief outline of the topics covered.

I. Sacrament of Mercy

   A. We need this sacrament when our lives start to sink

   B. Jesus reaches out to save us like he reached out to St. Peter

II. Theological Foundation for the Sacrament

   A. God is love (1 John 4:8)

      1. God's very nature is love—he is a community of Persons in the Trinity

      2. When we turn away from God's love, he seeks us out

   B. God's revelation of himself in Exodus 34:6 is mercy and steadfast love

   C. *Hesed,* Hebrew for "committed love" or "sustained love"

    D. Jesus is constantly going out in his public ministry to seek others

    E. John 20:19–23

        1. Jesus sends his Apostles out with authority to forgive sins

        2. They continue the ministry of reconciliation started by Jesus

        3. John 20:23—**"If you forgive the sins of any they are forgiven."**

    F. Second Corinthians 5:18–20—Paul and the other Apostles share in this ministry

        1. This authority is passed on from the Apostles to their successors

        2. The priest behind the priest: Jesus

        3. The priest acts in the Person of Christ the Head

III. Why Can't I Just Go to God Directly?

    A. We're all called to go straight to God every day

    B. Confession is the most direct way to go to God for his forgiveness

    C. God has always worked through mediators (Moses, Elijah, Elisha, the Apostles)

IV. Why Does It Make Sense That God Set up Confession This Way?

    A. It is very healthy to acknowledge mistakes and receive forgiveness

    B. God knows what we need

V. What Are the Effects of the Sacrament?

    A. We are reconciled with God (CCC 1468)

    B. We are reconciled with God's family, the Church (CCC 1469)

    C. We encounter the healing power of God's mercy

VI. Rite of Penance

A. First step is to prepare ahead of time with an examination of conscience

B. Confess our sins and sincerely try to remember all of them

C. Penance is an expression of love after receiving the free gift of forgiveness

D. Words of absolution—Jesus is present, and he is the one forgiving us of our sins

VII. Woman Caught in Adultery as an Image of Confession

A. Jesus did not condemn her in her sin

B. He loved her too much to leave her in her sin: "Go and sin no more."

"Forgiveness of sins brings reconciliation with God, but also with the Church."
—CCC 1462

DISCUSS

1. Matt had been away from Confession for seven years. He had been living far from God and came to a breaking point. Not knowing where to turn, he went to the parish and got in line for Confession. He writes about his experience: "When I heard the words of absolution from the priest, it was as if heavy chains fell away from my body. I experienced a sense of freedom and joy that I had never known. That was nearly twenty years ago, and today, I am still that changed man! How does Matt's story emphasize our psychological need and spiritual need of the sacrament?

_____

_____

2. In *The Fate of Empires and the Search for Survival,* historian Sir John Bagot Glubb (1897-1987) chronicles the decline and collapse of great empires and identifies a similar cycle in all. In the beginning, collective self-sacrifice and discipline builds the empire. Prosperity follows and leads to greater comfort, less religious practice, and moral decline. Finally, moral decline leads to selfishness, decadent living, and eventual collapse. How does this cycle demonstrate the corporate nature of sin and the need for the Sacrament of Reconciliation?

_____

_____

3. Jesus says to the woman caught in adultery: **"Neither do I condemn you; go, and do not sin again"** [John 8:11]. His words demonstrate that God loves us just as we are but too much to leave us there! Why is it not enough to say that "God loves you just as you are?"

_____

_____

_____

COMMIT—*ENCOUNTERING GOD'S MERCY*

The story of the prodigal son is perhaps one the most familiar of the many parables that Jesus tells. This narrative of sin, repentance, and forgiveness is a wonderful illustration of how we can encounter God in Confession. Read through this passage slowly and prayerfully:

> "There was a man who had two sons; and the younger of them said to his father, 'Father, give me the share of property that falls to me.' And he divided his living between them. Not many days later, the younger son gathered all he had and took his journey into a far country, and there he squandered his property in loose living. And when he had spent everything, a great famine arose in that country, and he began to be in want. So he went and joined himself to one of the citizens of that country, who sent him into his fields to feed swine. And he would gladly have fed on the pods that the swine ate; and no one gave him anything. But when he came to himself he said, 'How many of my father's hired servants have bread enough and to spare, but I perish here with hunger! I will arise and go to my father, and I will say to him, 'Father, I have sinned against heaven and before you; I am no longer worthy to be called your son; treat me as one of your hired servants.' And he arose and came to his father. But while he was yet at a distance, his father saw him and had compassion, and ran and embraced him and kissed him. And the son said to him, 'Father, I have sinned against heaven and before you; I am no longer worthy to be called your son.' But the father said to his servants, 'Bring quickly the best robe, and put it on him; and put a ring on his hand, and shoes on his feet; and bring the fatted calf and kill it, and let us eat and make merry; for this my son was dead, and is alive again; he was lost, and is found.' And they began to make merry."
>
> —Luke 15:11–24

Consider the younger son at the beginning of this parable. When he asks for his share of the inheritance, he is basically telling his father, "I prefer what you have to who you are—I want your stuff, but I don't want you anymore." **How do you think this made the father feel?**

_____

_____

_____

When the son had squandered his inheritance, he quickly realized how empty his chosen lifestyle was. He wanted to go home, but he felt like his poor choices were in the way of returning to the way things were. **How is this like (or unlike) our experience of sin?**

_____

_____

The father must have been watching for his son because he saw him "while he was yet at a distance." This loving and compassionate father couldn't wait for his son to make it all the way home, so he ran to meet him. And he was so eager to forgive him and welcome him home that he didn't even let his son finish the apology he had planned out. It was enough that his son desired to come home. **How do you think the son felt when his father welcomed him in this way? Have you had a similar experience in your life that you would be willing to share with us?**

_____

_____

In the Sacrament of Reconciliation, our Lord watches for us and runs to meet us. It is enough that we desire to come home. When we come to the sacrament with sorrow for our sins, God welcomes us home and wraps us in his grace. We were dead, and now we are alive again. We were lost, and now we are found.

Make an appointment with God to encounter his loving mercy in the Sacrament of Reconciliation. Find a time when you can go to Confession. Write it down. And begin preparing now and praying for the grace of a good confession.

_____

_____

> *"Forgiveness of sins brings reconciliation with God, but also with the Church."*
>
> **—CCC 1462**

CLOSING PRAYER

To you, O LORD, I lift up my soul.
O my God, in you I trust, let me not be put to shame;
let not my enemies exult over me.

Make me to know your ways, O LORD; teach me your paths.
Lead me in your truth, and teach me, for you are the God of my salvation;
for you I wait all the day long.
Be mindful of your compassion, O LORD, and of your merciful love,
for they have been from of old.
Remember not the sins of my youth, or my transgressions;
according to your mercy remember me, for your goodness' sake, O LORD!
Good and upright is the LORD; therefore he instructs sinners in the way.
He leads the humble in what is right, and teaches the humble his way.
All the paths of the LORD are mercy and faithfulness,
for those who keep his covenant and his testimonies.
For your name's sake, O LORD, pardon my guilt, for it is great.

Turn to me and be gracious to me; for I am lonely and afflicted.
Relieve the troubles of my heart, and bring me out of my distresses.
Consider my affliction and my trouble, and forgive all my sins.

Amen.

—Psalm 25:1–2, 4–11, 16–18

FOR FURTHER STUDY

Catechism of the Catholic Church, 1420–1498

NOTES

It's not about what it
It's about *Who* it is.

Prepare yourself and your family to receive Jesus in the Eucharist as never before with *Presence: The Mystery of the Eucharist*. World-renowned Catholic presenters unveil the truth and beauty behind the "source and summit" of the Christian life, from its origins in Sacred Scripture, to its profound role in the life of the Church and its members.

Learn more at AugustineInstitute.org/Presence

Presence™
THE MYSTERY OF THE EUCHARIST

 AUGUSTINE INSTITUTE